The KING and the SHEPHERD BOY

Written by **SAM BREWSTER**

Illustrated by **HANNAH GREEN**

10

The king and the shepherd boy gazed above
At a beautiful starlit night.
The shepherd boy dozed as the Eastern king rose
For one star was unusually bright.

He ran to his friends with their
scrolls and their pens
(In truth they were Magi, not kings).

COME QUICK!
LET US HURRY!

Too long have we studied!
This star can mean only one thing!
One thing, one thing,
This star can mean only one thing!"

Meanwhile on the hill all was perfectly still,
Though the shepherd boy noisily snored,
When **FLASH** in the night came a

DAZZLING LIGHT

As an angel appeared from the Lord!
He woke with a start and a
    fast-beating heart.

"*FEAR NOT!*"
said the angel (in vain).
"Hear news of great joy! A new baby boy!
YOUR SAVIOUR!
And CHRIST is his name!
His name, his name,
Your saviour and
CHRIST is his name!"

A saviour? thought he,
as he steadied his sheep
(It was all a bit much for his nerves).
Had he actually said, "a *MANGER* his bed"!?

There was just one thing for it: a

SEARCH!

So off the boy ran...

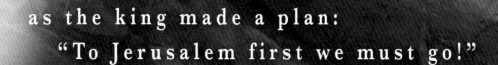

as the king made a plan:
"To Jerusalem first we must go!"

"We've come from afar
in pursuit of this star,
Come Herod! Please
say what you know!
You know, you know,

Come Herod! Please
say what you know!"

"A star? Tell me more!"
with a tightly clenched jaw
Said Herod, who feared it was true.

"A king you say?
Go and find him today.
And then tell me, I'll worship him too!"

The prophets had told in their writings of old
That Bethlehem town was the place.
So off the king sped, where the star brightly led
For there wasn't a moment to waste
To waste, to waste,
For there wasn't a moment to waste.

The boy shook his head, "Yes! A MANGER, I said!"
But they gave him the strangest of stares.

BETHLEHEM

So just to be sure,
    he tried one more door...

And gasped! For the baby was there!
He knew it was true, but knew not what to do,
So he stood with a quizzical grin.

Said Mary, "Hello! There's a shepherd, you know!"
And so Joseph welcomed him in,
Him in, him in,
And so Joseph welcomed him in.

"I know it sounds weird, but an angel appeared."
"Did he really? He spoke with us too!

He said, 'Call him Jesus, for soon he will free us
From sin' (all the bad things we do)."

But Joseph was stopped by a rather loud

So the shepherd boy opened the door...

The strangest of things!
Some richly dressed kings!

Said the boy, "What have *you* come here for?
Here for, here for?"

Said the boy,
    "What have you come here for?"

The dazzling kings looked around at the scene
With a palpable shock at the hay!
"They all look so poor!
What's this shepherd here for?"
Thought the king,
Have we come the wrong way?

So Mary said, "Maybe you're here for the baby?
He's here! Come over and see!"

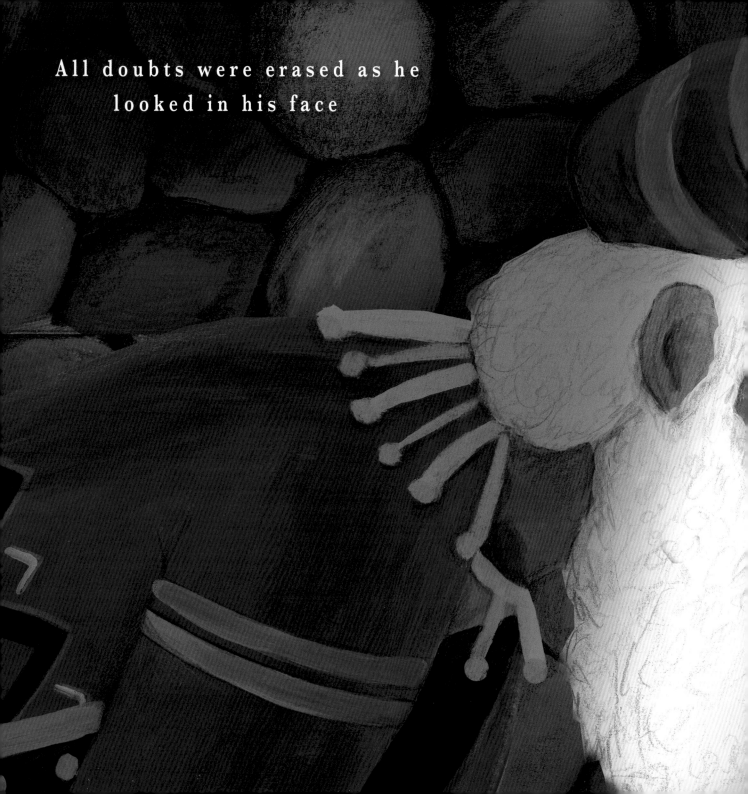

All doubts were erased as he
looked in his face

For he knew
here's the saviour for me,
For me, for me,

For he knew
here's the saviour for me.

The king and the shepherd boy left that day
With a song rising up in their hearts.
On meeting that night they were nothing alike
But now nothing could keep them apart.
For the saviour they'd seen came for
SHEPHERDS and KINGS,

Came to die for the great and the small.
They'd both messed up, but were equally loved,
That's why God sent a saviour for all
For all, for all,
That's why God sent a

SAVIOUR for all!

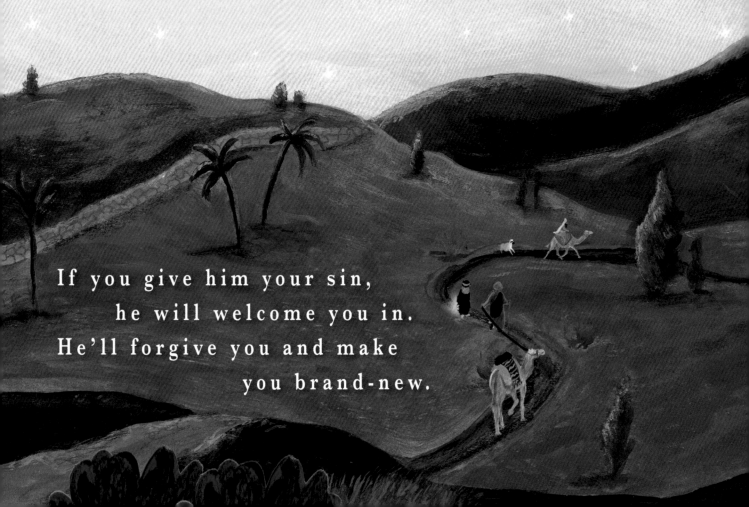

As they happily chat on their journey back,
Will you go to Bethlehem too?
The child they discovered
   still knows us and loves us,

HE CAME AS A SAVIOUR FOR YOU!

If you give him your sin,
   he will welcome you in.
He'll forgive you and make
   you brand-new.

So, whoever you are, will you follow the star
And ask him to save you too?

You too, you too?
And ask him to save you too?

You can read the original Bible stories in
Luke chapter 2 and Matthew chapter 2.

*In the Biblical accounts, the wise men visited Jesus
at a later stage to the shepherds – we hope this
retelling (with some artistic license) imaginatively
captures how Jesus came as a saviour for everyone.*

For my children, Amelie, Jo-Jo and Barney.
May you each discover Jesus as your saviour.

Published by 10Publishing, a division of 10ofThose Limited.

ISBN: 978-1-913896-60-7

10Publishing, a division of 10ofthose.com, Unit C, Tomlinson Road, Leyland, Lancashire, PR25 2DY England
Email: info@10ofthose.com   Website: www.10ofthose.com

Publishing
a division of 10 of those.com

10Publishing is committed to publishing
quality Christian resources that are biblical,
accessible and point people to Jesus.

www.10ofthose.com is our online retail partner
selling thousands of quality books at discounted prices.

For information contact: info@10ofthose.com
or check out our website: www.10ofthose.com